A Hairy Question

HAZEL EDWARDS

Illustrated by Rae Dale

sundance™

The Story Characters

Tina
She gets a haircut.

Jan
Tina's good friend.

Mom and Dad
Tina's parents.

Peter
Tina's brother.

The Story Setting

TABLE OF CONTENTS

CHAPTER 1

A Hairy Question

"Who cut your hair?" said one of the kids as I walked in the school gate.

"Did the rats get at your hair," said another, "or is it a bird's nest?"

I heard Ned say, "Tina, did you see Dracula?"

It was Monday morning, the first school day after my new haircut. I didn't want to be at school. I knew what kids were saying.

My hair looked terrible. One side was shorter than the other. The right side stuck out. The left side went under.

My friend Jan sat next to me.

"It doesn't look too bad," she said as we waited for Mr. Marsh, our teacher.

I didn't believe Jan. My new haircut
was all her fault. Jan had to say it
looked good. On Saturday, she had
cut my hair!

CHAPTER 2

Jan and Her Wild Ideas

Jan does some silly things. Cutting
my hair was one of her wild ideas.

My hair was very long. It was black and straight. It was so long, I could sit on it. I usually wore it tied back in a ponytail.

Jan has short, curly, brown hair. I thought it would be great to have curls like hers.

When we went swimming, Jan's hair dried fast. My hair took hours to dry.

Last Friday night we were at the pool.

"I wish my hair was like yours, Jan," I said after we got dressed. "Short hair is easy to take care of."

Jan looked up. She was drying
her hair.

"Why don't you get your hair cut, Tina?" she asked. "You could have a perm. That would give you some curls."

I shook my head. The wet ends of my hair dripped down my back.

"Cut your own hair," said Jan with a smile. "It's easy."

"I cut mine once," she added. "It looked all right. My hair just curled up by itself."

We shut our lockers and walked out of the locker room. I thought about a haircut.

My hair was still dripping down my back. Jan's curls were already dry.

"I bet I could cut your hair," said Jan.

CHAPTER 3

The Home Haircut

I wondered if I should let Jan do it.

"On Saturday, I could cut it. Then I could do a home perm for you," Jan offered.

On Saturday, Peter, my little brother, would be playing soccer. My Mom and Dad would be at our neighbor's house.

The house would be empty. So, I made up my mind.

"Okay, let's do it," I said.

That was my mistake. Letting Jan
cut my hair was a stupid idea.

At two o'clock, I could sit on my
hair. Then Jan began to cut. Snip.
Snip. Snip.

"I've never had it cut," I told Jan.

I watched Jan cutting my hair in the bathroom mirror. Snip. Snip. Snip.

Jan said, "You sure have a lot of hair."

"I used to!" I replied.

The bathroom floor was covered in long, black hair.

"Easy," said Jan as she cut. "Piece of cake!"

I remembered when Jan said cooking was easy. We spent hours scraping burned food off the stove.

Jan also told me that camping was easy. Then the tent fell on top of us during the night.

Camping

By three o'clock on Saturday afternoon, more hair was on the bathroom floor than on my head.

Ten years of hair was on the floor. I wanted it back. But it was too late!

"Look in the mirror," said Jan.

I did. There was a lot of face and not much hair.

"Is it all right?" Jan asked, looking worried.

What could I say? It was too late.

"One side is longer than the other," I said softly.

Jan cut some more. "Do you want some bangs?" she asked.

"All right," I said.

Jan cut even more. Snip. Snip. Snip.

"Take a look," said Jan.

In the mirror, I looked strange. My hair was gone. Bits stuck out all over the place.

Jan's face was pale.

"Shampoo it, then it will look better. Short hair dries fast," Jan said as she swept my ex-hair into a dustpan.

It did dry fast. But wisps of hair still stuck out.

"It will look better with curls," said Jan. She put my old hair into the kitchen trash. "Now for the perm."

CHAPTER 4

That Terrible Haircut

"Here's the package," said Jan. "Perms are easy. I brought some special rollers."

I shuddered.

What should I do? Could a perm be worse? . . . What would Dad say?

"No thanks, Jan. It might be worse,"
I said.

"It looks all right," said Jan. "It's just different. Let's try the rollers."

"Okay," I sighed.

At five o'clock Mom, Dad, and Peter came home. My hair was in rollers. None of them could tell how short it was.

"Take the trash out, please, Peter," said Mom.

"There's a pile of hair in here," Peter yelled.

"Shhh!" I whispered.

CHAPTER  5

What They Said

"Tina cut her hair off!" yelled Peter.

"What!" said Mom and Dad, rushing in to look.

I took out the rollers.

"Oh, Tina. Why did you do it?" asked Dad. "Your hair was beautiful."

Mom cried. I cried. Dad looked sad.

"You can have some of my hair,"
offered Peter. "You can stick it onto
yours."

He reached for the scissors. Mom
stopped him.

CHAPTER 6

Jan Has Another Idea

Monday was a bad day at school. Jan tried to cheer me up. She really is a good friend.

"Just act like you came up with a new fashion," she said.

I smiled.

"Let's make new clothes to wear with your new hair," said Jan. "It's easy to sew. I'll show you how to follow a pattern."

"No thanks, Jan. Let's go swimming instead. My hair will dry quickly now. That's one good thing."

Jan smiled. "But it is easy to sew."

I smiled back. "No thanks. I want to go swimming."

In about ten years, my hair will be long again. I might as well swim a lot while it's short.

GLOSSARY

different

not the same

Dracula

a scary monster

fault

responsibility
for a mistake

offer

to give
something nice

pattern
a cutout used to
make clothing

perm
makes hair curly
(short for permanent wave)

"piece of cake"
simple

shuddered
shook from
fear or cold

terrible
very bad, awful

Hazel Edwards

Hazel Edwards's hair changes sometimes. As author of over 130 books, Hazel is known for doing unusual things like hot-air ballooning or belly-dancing. *There's A Hippopotamus on Our Roof Eating Cake* is her best-known book. It is 21 years old this year.

Rae Dale

Rae Dale has taught in various schools. Now, painting and illustrating are her major interests, as well as reading, gardening, washing dishes, and collecting proverbs.

 sundance™

Copyright © 2000 Sundance/Newbridge, LLC

All rights reserved. No part of this publication may be reproduced, stored in a retrieval system or transmitted in any form or by any means, electronic, mechanical,photocopying, recording, or otherwise, without the prior written permission of the publisher.

Published by Sundance Publishing
33 Boston Post Road West, Suite 440, Marlborough, MA 01752
800-343-8204

Copyright © text Hazel Edwards
Copyright © illustrations Rae Dale

First published 1999 as Sparklers by
Blake Education, Locked Bag 2022, Glebe 2037, Australia
Exclusive United States Distribution: Sundance Publishing

ISBN: 978-0-7608-4938-5

Printed by Nordica International Ltd.
Manufactured in Guangzhou, China
May, 2012
Nordica Job#: CA21200579
Sundance/Newbridge PO#: 226970